Cover illustration by Lynn Breeze
Cover photograph by Kim Tonelli
Edited by Vronwyn M Thompson and Caroline Arthur
Designed by Brian Folkard Design

Copyright © 1994 The Guide Association
All rights reserved throughout the world.

Published in Great Britain by World International, an imprint of Egmont Publishing Ltd.,
Egmont House, PO Box 111,
Great Ducie Street, Manchester M60 3BL.
Printed in Italy.

ISBN 0-7498-1986-3

D0319856

£4.99
UK only

SUMMER SPECIAL

by Gillian Ellis   illustrations by Paula Martyr

'What shall we do for our Summer Special?' asked Brown Owl. The Brownies thought hard. Last year Brown Owl had taken them to the theme park and they had had a lovely time. Some of the Pack wanted to go again.

'Let's do something different,' said Tawny. Penny suggested the roller rink.

'Or ice-skating!' said Beth, excited. 'It looks easy on TV!'

'Don't you believe it!' said Snowy, remembering her last visit. 'That ice is ever so hard when you sit down suddenly!'

Katie had a good idea. 'How about the safari park?' she asked eagerly. 'My cousin says it's brilliant; you see wild animals!'

'Yes,' agreed Tania, her little sister. 'They have dolphins, too. I love dolphins.' The Brownies liked the sound of the safari park, so Brown Owl promised to book.

Tania's mum wasn't so sure about a whole day out.

'You're only just seven,' she said, doubtfully. 'You might find it too much. You were worn out that day we went to London.'

'Oh, Mum!' said Tania, making herself as tall as possible. 'I was only six then. I'm grown up now. And if Katie's going, so am I!'

Mum and Katie smiled at the determined little face.

'OK,' agreed Mum, 'you can both go. I'm sure it'll be great.'

The Brownies were very excited on the morning of the trip. Every single Brownie was there, trying not to make too much noise! Brown Owl had said that they must behave beautifully because they were going on a public coach; there weren't enough Brownies to hire one of their own.

The other passengers smiled when they saw the eager little girls scrambling on board. The coach trip was fun; the Brownies played a game on the way, counting all the red, blue and yellow cars to see which was the most popular colour. It seemed no time at all before they were arriving at the safari park. The coach driver drove very slowly in a long line of cars and coaches.

'Look out for elephants!' he said through his microphone, and sure enough, a herd of elephants ambled past. The Brownies knelt up on the seats to see better.

'See the giraffes!' squeaked Amy. 'I never knew they were so tall!'

'Look, Tawny!' gasped Penny. 'See those big things over there? They're fighting!' Sure enough, two huge rhinos were charging towards each other, crashing their great horns together. Again and again they charged – and what a noise they made!

'I wouldn't like to meet one of those on a dark night!' declared Snowy. The coach edged slowly forward and suddenly Beth gave a little yelp.

'Tawny! Look!' Right there at the window,

clinging to the side of the coach and staring straight at Beth, was a monkey with great big eyes.

'Can I open the window and stroke him?' asked Beth, thrilled.

'Definitely not!' said Brown Owl, firmly. 'He looks sweet, but I bet he can bite like anything!' Suddenly the coach was covered with monkeys, swarming everywhere and chattering angrily.

'Oi! Get off!' came the bus driver's voice, and the Brownies saw a large monkey, busily trying to remove the windscreen wiper from the front window! The girls burst out laughing, but Snowy put a warning finger to her lips.

'I don't think the driver thinks it's very funny,' she whispered.

There was so much to see. Katie and Tania could hardly believe it when the coach stopped right by a group of lions, lazily enjoying the sun. The male was enormous, with a huge bushy mane.

'That lioness looks just like my Silky at home!' marvelled Penny, 'only about a million times bigger.'

'Lions are a type of cat,' Tawny reminded them. 'They belong to the same family as Silky.'

'But I wouldn't advise you to try stroking them!' added Snowy, and looking at those huge claws and teeth, Penny had to agree.

The Brownies had a wonderful day. After the ride through the animal enclosure, they had a picnic in the open air, then spent an hour in the play park.

Next the Brownies saw the dolphin show. They sat on benches near a vivid turquoise pool where dolphins flashed swiftly about and leapt high out of the water. There was a seal, too, who played ball with the keeper, and clapped himself loudly every time he caught the ball on his shiny nose!

Even though the Brownies sat quite high up, they were sometimes splashed by the dolphins.

'Don't worry!' laughed Snowy, after one shower. 'You'll dry off in the sun.' After the show, Brown Owl bought everyone an ice-cream, then there were just ten minutes left for another visit to the swings. All too soon it was time to go home.

'Did you have a nice time?' asked Mum as she met Katie and Tania at the coach park. Katie nodded and skipped all the way home, telling Mum about all they'd seen. Tania was dragging her feet.

'Carry me, Mum,' she begged, and Mum smiled as she picked her up. 'Not quite so grown up as we thought!' she said, as Tania's head snuggled into her shoulder. But Tania didn't hear, she was already fast asleep.

The Brownie Story at your FINGERTIPS!

That's what you can have if you make our finger puppets and theatre. You can use the puppet theatre to teach a newcomer to your Pack the Brownie story, or just to remind yourself of what being a Brownie is all about. What's more, by making these puppets you could complete a Go! Challenge.

by Jane Wilson   illustrations by Anna King

Finger puppets

You will need:
Greaseproof paper or white tissue paper
Pencil
Pins
Scissors
Small pieces of felt in red, flesh, brown, blue, black, yellow, white and beige
Sewing thread in red, blue and beige
Embroidery thread in brown, red and blue
Two black or brown sequins (optional)
Needle

Preparing the pattern

Carefully trace all the shapes shown here onto greaseproof or tissue paper and cut them out. As they are so small it is a good idea to keep them in an envelope until you need them. When you are ready to cut out, pin each pattern piece on to the colour of felt required and cut carefully around the edge. Unpin and keep the pattern piece and the cut-out felt in the envelope until you are ready to sew. Some of the pattern pieces will be used more than once.

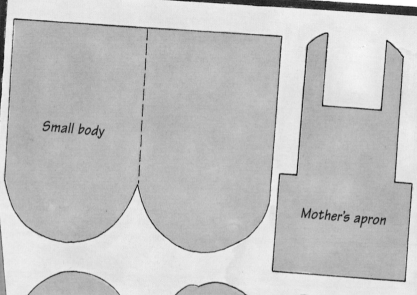

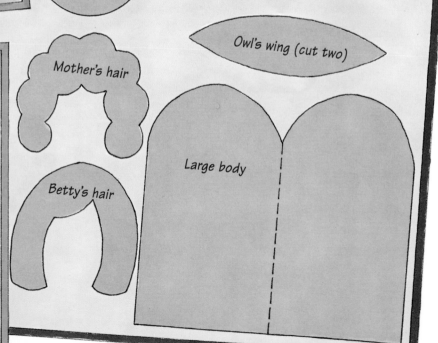

Small body

Mother's apron

Head

Tommy's hair

Owl's ear piece

Owl's wing (cut two)

Mother's hair

Betty's hair

Large body

To make Betty

Using the smaller body pattern, cut Betty's body out of red felt. Cut a head in flesh-coloured felt and Betty's hair in brown felt.

Fold the body piece in half and pin. Using red sewing thread and a small running stitch, carefully sew along the side and curved top of the shape, leaving the bottom open for your finger.

Glue Betty's hair in place on the head. Embroider her eyes in brown embroidery thread and her mouth in red embroidery thread.

Spread glue onto the bottom half of the back of the head and stick it to the curved top of the body.

To make Tommy

Using the smaller body pattern, cut Tommy's body out of blue felt. Cut a head in flesh-coloured felt and Tommy's hair in black felt.

Fold the body piece in half and pin. Using blue sewing thread and a small running stitch, carefully sew along the side and curved top of the shape, leaving the bottom open for your finger.

Glue Tommy's hair in place on the head. Embroider his eyes in blue embroidery thread and his mouth in red embroidery thread.

Spread glue onto the bottom half of the back of the head and stick it to the curved top of the body.

To make Mother

Using the larger body pattern, cut Mother's body out of blue felt. Cut a head in flesh-coloured felt, Mother's hair in yellow felt and her apron in white felt.

Fold the body piece in half and pin. Using blue sewing thread and a small running stitch, carefully sew along the side and curved top of the shape, leaving the bottom open for your finger. Glue Mother's apron on to her body. Glue Mother's hair in place on the head. Embroider her eyes in blue embroidery thread and her mouth in red embroidery thread.

Spread glue onto the bottom half of the back of the head and stick it to the curved top of the body.

To make the Wise Owl

Using the smaller body pattern, cut the owl's body out of beige felt. Cut a head in beige felt. Cut two wings and the ear piece in brown felt.

Fold the body piece in half and pin. Using beige sewing thread and a small running stitch, carefully sew along the side and curved top of the shape, leaving the bottom open for your finger. Glue a wing to each side of the body. Glue the ear piece in place on the head. Embroider the owl's beak in brown embroidery thread and stitch or glue on two sequins for the eyes. Spread glue on to the bottom half of the back of the head and stick it to the curved top of the body.

The colours suggested here are based on the illustrations in the Brownie Guide Handbook, but you could make your puppets any colour you like.

Theatre

You will need:
A large empty cereal box
Scissors
Ruler
Pencil
Brown paper
Glue
Card
Paints, felt-tipped pens
or crayons

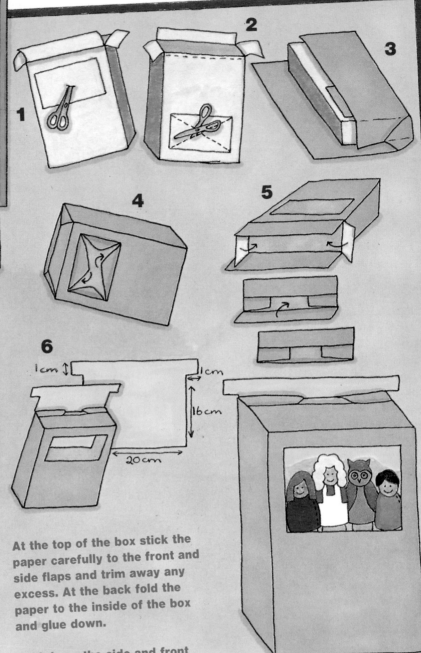

To make

Cut the back flap off the open top of the cereal box. Draw a line across the box 3cm below the top and two lines down the box 3cm in from each side. Draw another line across the box 10cm below the top line. You will need to cut out this rectangle to make the hole through which the puppets appear. To do this push the point of a pair of scissors carefully through the card in the centre of the rectangle, then cut out to the corners. When you have done this you will easily be able to cut along the lines.

Turn the box over and cut a hole of the same size in the back of the box at the bottom. This is for you to put your hand through.

Now cover the box with brown paper. Wrap the paper around the box as if you were wrapping a parcel, but glue the edge down instead of using sticky tape. Fold the paper at the bottom of the box as on a parcel and glue in place.

Carefully push the point of a pair of scissors through the brown paper aiming for the centre of each of the holes in the box. Cut to the corners of the rectangles, fold the paper to the inside and glue down.

At the top of the box stick the paper carefully to the front and side flaps and trim away any excess. At the back fold the paper to the inside of the box and glue down.

Fold down the side and front flaps and glue together. Put a weight such as a book on top of the box until the glue is dry.

To make scenery, draw on card a rectangle which is slightly narrower than your cereal box and as long as the distance from the top of the box to the top of the hole in the back (about 20cm x 16cm). Draw a strip 1cm deep and 1cm wider than the cereal box on the top of the rectangle and then cut out the shape. The card will fit through the slit in the top of your theatre and hang in place.

Using paints, felt-tipped pens or crayons, draw a suitable background onto the scenery. You will need several pieces of scenery to show each part of your play. For example, you could draw the wood, the pond and the inside of the cottage, untidy for the first scene and tidy once Tommy and Betty have learnt how to be Brownies.

Now everything is ready, turn down the lights, draw up the curtain and on with the show!

Do you know a single Brownie who doesn't like baked beans? I don't! But instead of just eating them on toast, why not try these beany recipes? Each one makes enough for four Brownies.

Before you begin:
- Wash your hands.
- Tie back long hair.

BEAN FEAST

by Brenda Apsley
illustrations by Lynn Breeze

Bean Bread

1 small French bread stick
440g tin baked beans
3 thick or 5 thin spring onions
4 tablespoons sage and onion dry stuffing mix

1 Pre-heat the oven to 190°C/375°F/gas mark 5.
2 Cut the ends off the bread stick. Using a big spoon pull all the soft bread out of the middle, taking care not to break the 'shell' of the loaf.
3 In a bowl, carefully add a little boiling water to the stuffing mix. The stuffing will 'swell', but should still be firm.
4 Use scissors to snip the spring onions into 1cm pieces. Stir them into the stuffing.
5 Carefully open the tin of beans and add to the stuffing mix. Add a little salt and pepper and mix well.
6 Pack the mixture into the bread 'shell'. Press the ends back on and wrap the loaf in kitchen foil.

7 Bake for 12–15 minutes. Cut into slices and eat hot or cold.

- Add 50g chopped ham or peanuts to the stuffing mix if you like.
- Use the bread for breadcrumbs – or give the birds a treat!

·BEANFACT·

In Britain we eat baked beans worth more than £230 million every year.

Cracker Bean Quiche

18 crackers - 9 cream crackers and 9 mixed grain crackers
198g tub cheese spread
440g tin baked beans and sausages

1 Pre-heat the oven to 180°C/350°F/gas mark 4.
2 Put the crackers into a plastic bag and hit them with the (unopened!) bean tin until they are crushed into little pieces.
3 In a bowl, mix the cracker pieces and the cheese spread. Mash them with a spoon until the mixture is smooth.
4 Use your fingers to press the mixture into a 15cm shallow flan or cake tin.
5 Cut the sausages into 2cm pieces. Pour the beans and sausage pieces over the cracker base.
6 Bake for 12-15 minutes.
7 Eat hot with a baked potato, or cold with salad.

·BEANFACT·

Baked beans are good for you - they are low in fat and high in fibre. Try reduced sugar beans.

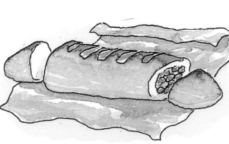

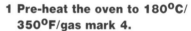

Beany Faces

225g plain flour
100g soft margarine
Salt
75g Cheddar cheese
1 large 'beef' tomato
4 mushrooms
440g tin baked beans

1 Pre-heat the oven to 190°C/ 375°F/gas mark 5.
2 Sieve the flour and a pinch of salt into a mixing bowl.
3 Use your fingertips to rub the margarine into the flour. Stop when the mixture looks like breadcrumbs.
4 Grate the cheese. Stir it into the flour and margarine mixture.
5 Make the mixture into dough by adding cold water. Add a tablespoon at a time and mix with a round-ended knife. Add only enough water to make a stiff dough – it should not be wet and sloppy.
6 On a floured worktop, use a rolling pin to roll out the pastry to about 5mm thick. Cut out 10cm circles, using a pastry cutter or glass tumbler. You should get between 12 and 16 pastry circles.
7 Put the pastry circles on a greased baking sheet. Bake for 12-15 minutes.
8 Cut each mushroom into four slices.
9 Cut the tomato into thin slices. Take out the seeds and cut each ring in half.
10 When the pastry circles are cooked, spoon the beans on the top halves of the circles for hair. Add two mushroom slice eyes, and a tomato slice mouth.
11 Put the faces back in the oven for 5-8 minutes until the beans are warm.

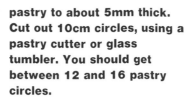

Bean Paté

440g tin baked beans

1 Tip the beans into a sieve over a bowl. Drain off the sauce.
2 Put the beans into a bowl and mash with a fork until you have a smooth mixture. If it is too hard, add a spoonful of sauce.

- Eat the bean paté on crackers, slices of French bread or tortilla chips.
- Use the paté as a dip for small pieces of raw vegetables.
- Use the paté as a sandwich filling. Add some chopped celery, chopped hard-boiled egg or chopped apple to the paté if you like.

Cowgirl Beef 'n' Beans

1 onion
450g minced beef
400g tin chopped tomatoes
2 teaspoons sweet paprika
440g tin baked beans
Salt and pepper

For the topping:
3 slices of thick-cut bread
Butter or margarine

1 Peel and chop the onion finely.
2 Put the minced beef and onion in a large pan over a medium heat. Fry for 10 minutes until the meat is brown and crumbly.
3 Add the tomatoes, paprika, salt, pepper and baked beans to the pan. Bring the mixture to the boil, put on a lid and simmer over a low heat for 30 minutes. Stir the mixture from time to time.
4 Near the end of the cooking time, turn on the grill.
5 Butter each slice of bread on both sides. Cut into 3cm cubes.
6 Put the beef 'n' beans into a serving dish. Put the buttered bread cubes on top. Grill for 5 to 8 minutes, until the bread cubes are golden brown.

• Use the beef 'n' beans mixture to fill baked potatoes.
• Be a Mexican cowgirl and pile the mixture into taco shells.

You don't have to eat beans hot. Try them in a salad.

Beany Salad

225g tin baked beans
50g mushrooms
2 sticks celery
Half a red pepper
Half a small cauliflower

For the dressing:
2 tablespoons lemon juice
1 dessertspoon Worcester sauce
Salt and pepper

1 Cut the cauliflower into tiny 'florets'.
2 Wipe the mushrooms and slice each one into 4.
3 Cut the celery into 1cm chunks.
4 Take the seeds from the pepper. Cut the flesh into tiny cubes.
5 Put the beans in a sieve and drain off most of the sauce.
6 Mix everything gently in a big bowl.
7 Put the lemon juice, Worcester sauce and some salt and black pepper into a glass bottle or jar with a screw-top lid. Put on the lid and shake.
8 Pour the dressing over the salad and toss gently so everything is coated.

PETAL POSER

Each of these flowers has the jumbled-up name of a flower in its petals. Can you arrange the letters in the right order to find them?

Puzzle TIME

by Marion Thompson illustrations by Jane Hibbert

SEED HUNT

This hungry bird can't find its way to the food. Can you help it to get through the maze to have a feast?

The answers are on page 61

The editor managed to catch up with Brownies on holiday at Blackland Farm in Sussex... but only just!

Photographs by Lucy Drew

Postcards from Pack Holiday

Having a swinging time...

The gang's all here...

'We've been doing archery, and abseiling, and rock climbing, and swimming... and making kites!'

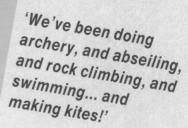

14

'Brown Owl says next year we can do Pack Holiday under canvas!'

Wise Owl seems to be having a good time too!

Time for one last sing-song before we go home...

With thanks to Brownies of the 7th Gillingham and 1st North Cray Packs and their Guiders and helpers.

CONCERT TIME!

by Gillian Ellis
illustrations by Lisa Berkshire

Have you ever thought of putting on your own concert? Does it sound impossible? You've probably been in concerts arranged by Brown Owl, where she told you what to do; maybe you think you couldn't manage it without her?

Not at all! If you plan your show very carefully, it could be a real success, but you must leave yourself plenty of time to rehearse and begin gathering everything you need right away.

First decide what you each do best! There's no point in Sarah reciting if she forgets every other line, or in Jenny being the lead in a play if she can't speak above a whisper! Each choose one main thing such as singing, acting, miming, dancing, reciting, playing an instrument or working a puppet which you are confident about, preferably something you've already performed in public, perhaps at a school concert.

Keep it simple! If you're singing, pick a song with not too many verses, and learn the words and tune thoroughly. Choose music to suit your voice, not too high, not too low, and practise till you could sing it in your sleep! Make sure your pianist or guitarist, if any, can be there on the day of the concert, and have as many rehearsals with her as possible.

The same tips apply to dancing or playing instruments, especially the one about practising until you know the piece inside out! For dancers, a further warning; vary your dance as much as possible. Audiences are quickly bored by a routine composed of four steps repeated again and again to a tape lasting five minutes!

If you choose to act, mime or work puppets, you'll probably do it with others, so rehearsals are especially important. You may not realise that Brown Owl comes to Brownies with carefully planned meetings, so do ask her in advance for time to rehearse. The best time may be during Journey work.

Choose a play or mime that is not too difficult, without long speeches to learn. If you need costumes, think about your own wardrobes or dressing-up boxes. It's all very well having St George and the Dragon, but suits of armour and dragon scales aren't always easy to find! On the other hand, if your mum has a silver dress and your brother will lend you his balaclava helmet, all you need is a pair of woolly tights and you're away – as long as you have a large green curtain for the dragon!

If you invent your own play, give your plot a definite shape and a definite end! There's nothing worse than a home-made play which starts well, but rambles on and tails off! Don't perform it like the make-believe games you play in the school lunch-hour; the two things are totally different. Your play must have proper words and you must rehearse them well.

If you decide on a puppet show, don't try to read the script and work the puppet at the same time! Either let one Brownie read and another work each puppet, or make sure you know your lines by heart!

Music is important for your concert. To set the atmosphere as the audience arrives, have some taped music playing, but not too loudly.

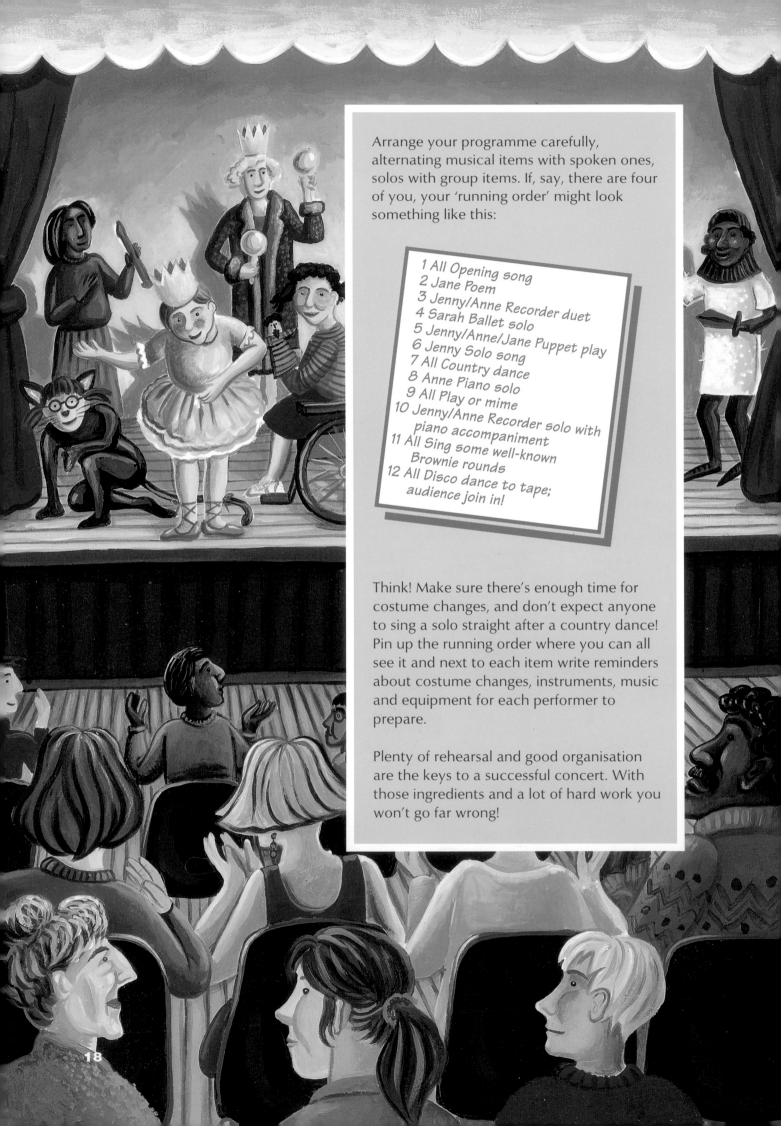

Arrange your programme carefully, alternating musical items with spoken ones, solos with group items. If, say, there are four of you, your 'running order' might look something like this:

1 All Opening song
2 Jane Poem
3 Jenny/Anne Recorder duet
4 Sarah Ballet solo
5 Jenny/Anne/Jane Puppet play
6 Jenny Solo song
7 All Country dance
8 Anne Piano solo
9 All Play or mime
10 Jenny/Anne Recorder solo with piano accompaniment
11 All Sing some well-known Brownie rounds
12 All Disco dance to tape; audience join in!

Think! Make sure there's enough time for costume changes, and don't expect anyone to sing a solo straight after a country dance! Pin up the running order where you can all see it and next to each item write reminders about costume changes, instruments, music and equipment for each performer to prepare.

Plenty of rehearsal and good organisation are the keys to a successful concert. With those ingredients and a lot of hard work you won't go far wrong!

A NEW START FOR LUCY?

by Heather Welford
illustrations by Celia Chester

*T*here was the usual clatter, chatter and bustle as the Brownies gathered up their coats and ran to the door to meet waiting parents.

'Don't forget, Brownies,' Brown Owl's voice came above the noise. 'Say goodbye to Lucy. You won't see her next week. She'll be miles and miles away!'

''Bye, Lucy,' came a chorus.

Lucy zipped her coat and tried to smile back.

She walked home with Mum, not saying anything.

'You're a bit quiet tonight,' said Mum, gently. 'Are you thinking about tomorrow?'

'Yes,' Lucy's voice was almost a whisper. 'I think I'm a bit worried.'

Her mother understood at once.

'Look, Lucy,' she said, 'I can't tell you not to be worried. Moving house and going such a long way away is a bit worrying for me, too. But I can promise that in time, things'll work out.'

'Are you worried as well, then?' Lucy looked up at her mother, surprised.

She knew Mum worried about things like crossing the road, violin practice and having enough change to put in the parking meter – but she'd never imagined Mum worrying about moving house.

They'd got to their door by now. Mum turned the key.

'Of course I'm worried. And Dad is, too. We're both starting a new job.'

Lucy thought about this as she ate her supper that night.

Mum and Dad's new job was worrying and exciting, she decided. In fact, it was the best bit – maybe the only good bit – about

19

moving. Running a newspaper shop in a small village was bound to be fun, wasn't it? And they'd sell sweets, and birthday cards, and cheap toys... and Lucy, Dad had said, might be able to help out from time to time.

'Mum,' she said later, when Mum had come in to say goodnight (for the last time in this room, Lucy thought), 'you promise things will work out?'

'In time – I promise,' said Mum. 'The shop will give us all a new start, you'll see.' And she gave Lucy an extra long, reassuring cuddle.

●

Two weeks later, Lucy hovered at the door of the village hall, hanging onto Mum's hand. A round-faced lady came up to them.

'Hello,' she said, smiling. 'I'm Fiona Sutton, Brown Owl. You must be Mrs Trench and Lucy. We spoke on the 'phone.'

Mum smiled back. 'Yes, that's right. Lucy's hoping there'll be some girls from her new school here.'

Brown Owl looked doubtful. 'Mm. You go to Bedewell, don't you, Lucy? Most of the girls here are from Belmont Primary. Bedewell girls tend to go to St Mary's Brownies – it's nearer to where most of them live.'

Lucy's heart sank.

Belmont was actually the nearest school to their house, and it wasn't surprising most children in the village went there.

But when Mum and Dad were arranging new schools, Bedewell was the only one with a place, and Lucy had ended up there instead. It was a car ride away, and she hadn't met anyone who lived nearby. The children were friendly, Lucy had told herself, but she still felt very new indeed.

It was the same at Brownies. Brown Owl was very kind, and the Brownies tried to make her feel welcome. But they all seemed to know each other so well.

'I don't fit in anywhere,' Lucy told Mum that night. 'Everyone's friendly, but they don't

want to be my friend, if you know what I mean.'

Lucy remembered her Brownie friends back home – she still thought of her old house as 'home' – Abigail, Sarah, Emma, Joanna... and how she knew several of them at her old school, as well. Joanna and Emma sat at the same table. But though her best friend at home, Katy, had written, Lucy longed for someone nearer.

At half-past eight the next morning, Lucy was just finishing her toast. Dad was standing at the table, slurping his tea, grabbing a quick bit of breakfast before driving Lucy to school. Mum was serving in the shop.

'Will you do me a favour, Lucy, when we're in the car?' asked Dad. 'I want to stop at that house by the farm. I forgot to put their *Farmers Weekly* in the paper boy's bag this morning – and I can't afford to make mistakes with new customers. Will you run out and stick it through their door on the way?'

Lucy nodded. 'But we'd better get going soon, Dad, or I'll be late.'

●

Dad pulled up the car outside his customer's house, and Lucy jumped out.

'I'll turn the car round while you're doing that,' Dad said. 'Then we won't lose much time.'

Lucy got to the front door, along a long, winding path. The letter box was quite high

up, just too high for her to reach and put the paper through. She stood on tiptoe and st..ret..ched..., but it was no good. She could just touch it, but not enough to push it open very far.

Suddenly, the door opened and Lucy almost fell into the house.

'Whaa...whooooops!' said a giggling, happy voice. 'I heard someone rattling and came to see what was up. Hey, you're the girl who came to Brownies last week, aren't you? Is that my dad's *Farmers Weekly*? Great! He was

already saying it should've come today. Why've you brought it? Oh, yes, your family have the newsagent's, now, don't they?'

There was a sudden silence as the girl stopped talking at last and waited for Lucy to answer.

'Yes,' Lucy stammered. 'You're right.' She couldn't think of anything to say. Then she remembered. 'You're Caroline, aren't you?'

'Right!' answered Caroline. She looked at Lucy's uniform. 'Oh, you go to Bedewell. I go to Rindwood Primary – miles away. But when we moved here, I didn't really want to change schools, too. Don't know if I did the right thing, though. No-one round here goes there.'

'Not even anyone at Brownies?' asked Lucy.

'No. They're mostly at Belmont.'

Lucy heard the toot-toot of her dad's horn. She jumped.

'That's my dad,' she said. 'I'm on my way to school.'

'Listen,' said Caroline. 'Bedewell's on the way to Rindwood, you know. Maybe you could come with us some time and we'd drop you off...'

Lucy hesitated. 'Well... it's up to Mum and Dad.' But she was thinking she'd like to, very much. 'I'll ask them!' she said brightly.

'Well, we'll talk about it at Brownies, shall we?' said Caroline. 'And maybe you can come round for tea or something...'

'Caroline really looks hopeful,' Lucy thought. 'She wants me to say yes.'

Toot, toot! Dad was getting impatient.

With a cheerful nod at Caroline's suggestion, and a wave, Lucy ran down the path and into the car. For the first time in a fortnight, she felt things were working out after all.

'Dad,' she said, grinning, 'I think I've found someone who wants to be my friend, and her name's Caroline.'

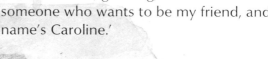

Canadian PUZZLES

by Jane Wilson   illustrations by Jane Hibbert

Hello! I'm a Brownie from Canada. As you can see I wear a sash with my badges on just like you do, but underneath I wear a brown sweatshirt or striped t-shirt and I tie my orange scarf in a reef knot instead of wearing a woggle. In Canada we can join Brownies when we are six years old and we go on to Guides when we are nine. We make a Promise very similar to yours and our Promise badge shows a Brownie man on a bar. We work for badges called the Golden Bar, Golden Ladder and Golden Hand which are like the Footpath, Road and Highway. We also like to gain Interest Badges.

Would you like to visit us in Canada one day? These puzzles will help you to find out more about our country. It is very beautiful and you will find lots to explore as it is also very big. In fact, Canada is the second largest country in the world, stretching from the Atlantic Ocean to the Pacific Ocean and spanning five time zones. This means that a Brownie on the Atlantic coast might be setting off for her Pack meeting at the same time as a Brownie on the Pacific coast is just finishing her lunch!

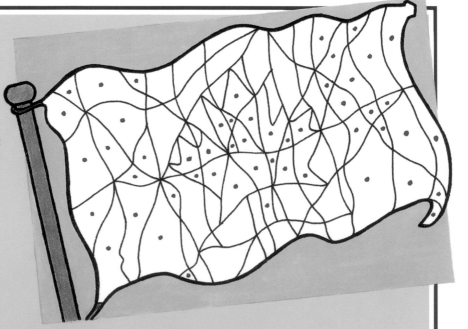

Eastern Canada is famous for its maple trees. We Brownies love these because they have a sugary sap which can be collected from the trees in spring and boiled to make maple syrup – delicious on ice-cream, pancakes or waffles! The leaf of the maple tree is the symbol of our Canadian flag. If you colour all the shapes with a dot in them red you will see what it looks like.

For many hundreds of years our country was occupied by the Innuit people (the proper name for Eskimos) in the north and by Indian tribes in the south. From the fifteenth century onwards, explorers from Europe arrived and, finding a good supply of beaver furs which were very valuable, began to settle. They also found fertile fishing grounds and fishing is still an important industry in Canada today.

About half of modern Canadians are descended from British settlers and a third from French settlers. In the province of Quebec, which is where the French explorers set up their trading posts, four fifths of the population still speak French as their first language. The other fifth of our people trace their ancestry back to nations all over the world.

Here is a map of Canada. We have marked our major cities, including our capital Ottawa, on it for you. But, perhaps because of our mixed ethnic background, some of our other place names are much more colourful and we have left you to guess these for yourself. You will find the answers on page 61.

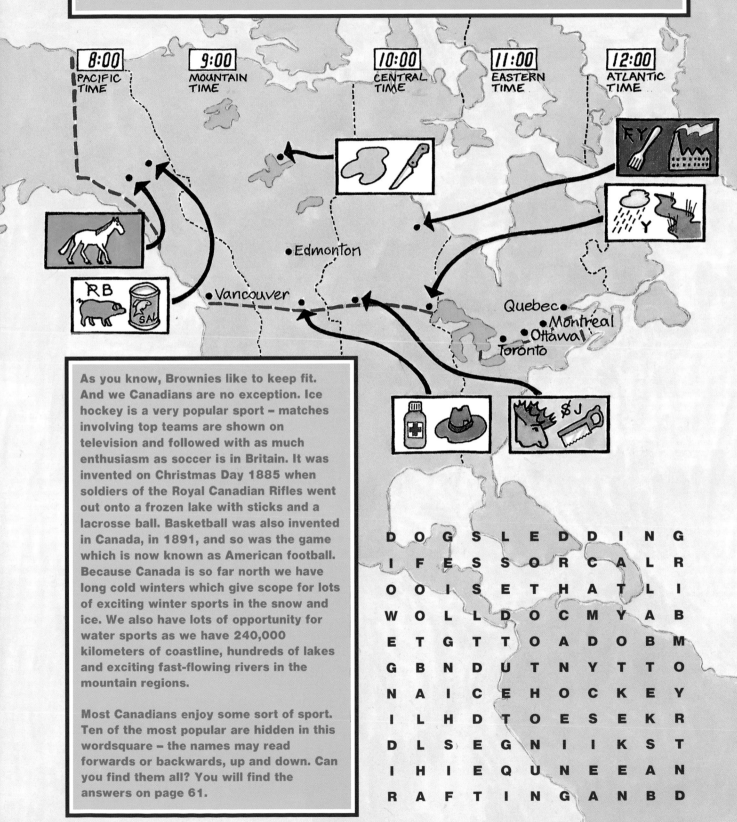

As you know, Brownies like to keep fit. And we Canadians are no exception. Ice hockey is a very popular sport – matches involving top teams are shown on television and followed with as much enthusiasm as soccer is in Britain. It was invented on Christmas Day 1885 when soldiers of the Royal Canadian Rifles went out onto a frozen lake with sticks and a lacrosse ball. Basketball was also invented in Canada, in 1891, and so was the game which is now known as American football. Because Canada is so far north we have long cold winters which give scope for lots of exciting winter sports in the snow and ice. We also have lots of opportunity for water sports as we have 240,000 kilometers of coastline, hundreds of lakes and exciting fast-flowing rivers in the mountain regions.

Most Canadians enjoy some sort of sport. Ten of the most popular are hidden in this wordsquare – the names may read forwards or backwards, up and down. Can you find them all? You will find the answers on page 61.

```
D O G S L E D D I N G
I F E S S O R C A L R
O O I S E T H A T L I
W O L L D O C M Y A B
E T G T T O A D O B M
G B N D U T N Y T T O
N A I C E H O C K E Y
I L H D T O E S E K R
D L S E G N I I K S T
I H I E Q U N E E A N
R A F T I N G A N B D
```

stretching

Waking up
in the morning
is lovely.
Especially when you s-t-r-e-t-c-h.
You open up
your legs and arms
and stretch.
It's just lovely.
The feeling just makes
you want to do it
over and over again.
But after a while
your stretch
runs out
and it's over.

by Sharon Cheeks
illustration by
Sarah Hedley

Reprinted with the
kind permission of the
National Exhibition of Children's Art

Where would you be without your feet? You need them for so many things – to balance and support your body, as well as for running, walking, skipping, jumping, dancing and lots of other things.

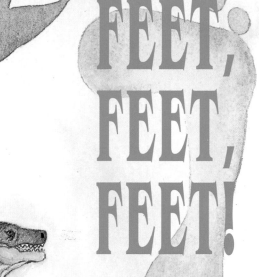

FEET, FEET, FEET!

by Libby Coolson
illustrations by
Gini Wade

First feet

Dinosaurs were the first creatures with real feet. Fossil footprints have been found that are about 150 million years old. Apatosaurus was one of the 'lizard feet' dinosaurs. He had big, flat feet on legs like huge tree trunks. You could probably lie down in one of his footprints!

Some scientists called palaeontologists can tell a lot about dinosaurs from their footprints. They know that long, sharp nails on the toes (talons) mean the dinosaur was probably a meat eater and far-apart footprints are a sign of a fast runner.

Flying feet

Bird feet are designed for what birds do with them. Birds that perch (sit) in trees, like sparrows and blue tits, have three front toes and one back one, so they can grip tightly and not fall off!

Woodpeckers have two toes pointing forward and two pointing back. These help them cling to tree trunks as they search for food.

Grouse and pheasants live on the ground and have strong feet for running fast.

Tiny hummingbirds don't walk, so their feet are very thin and weak.

Ducks and other water birds have webbed feet. Skin flaps between the toes are like little paddles and help them to swim well.

Birds that hunt for food, like owls, have very strong feet with long nails (called talons) on their toes, so they can grip prey like mice.

Penguins live in the cold Antarctic. They keep their eggs on their feet, holding them away from the cold snow. The chicks are kept warm on their feet too.

The ostrich is the largest bird. It is too heavy to fly, but it is the fastest creature on two legs. Its feet are very strong, with two toes.

Fossil feet

Humans' ancestors changed from walking on four legs to two about four million years ago. Fossil footprints have been found in Africa. We know they are made by humans because only men and women have feet with heel pads and big toes. Footprints left by girls so long ago are just the same shape as yours.

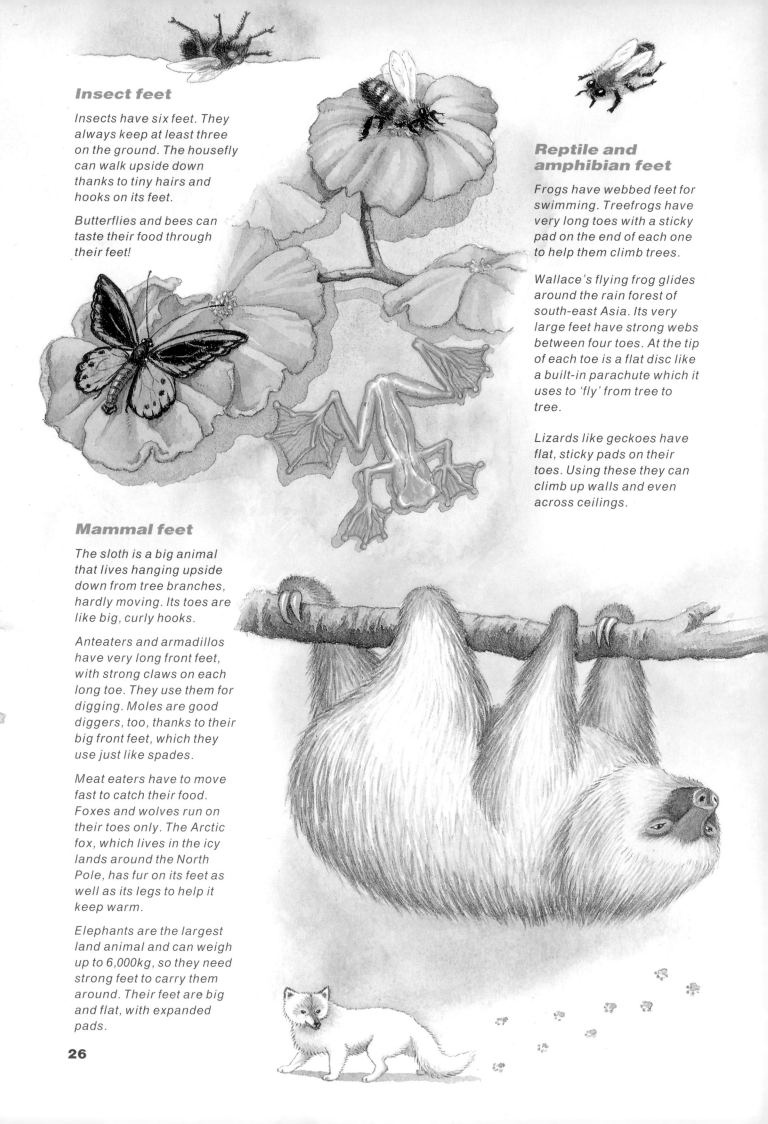

Insect feet

Insects have six feet. They always keep at least three on the ground. The housefly can walk upside down thanks to tiny hairs and hooks on its feet.

Butterflies and bees can taste their food through their feet!

Reptile and amphibian feet

Frogs have webbed feet for swimming. Treefrogs have very long toes with a sticky pad on the end of each one to help them climb trees.

Wallace's flying frog glides around the rain forest of south-east Asia. Its very large feet have strong webs between four toes. At the tip of each toe is a flat disc like a built-in parachute which it uses to 'fly' from tree to tree.

Lizards like geckoes have flat, sticky pads on their toes. Using these they can climb up walls and even across ceilings.

Mammal feet

The sloth is a big animal that lives hanging upside down from tree branches, hardly moving. Its toes are like big, curly hooks.

Anteaters and armadillos have very long front feet, with strong claws on each long toe. They use them for digging. Moles are good diggers, too, thanks to their big front feet, which they use just like spades.

Meat eaters have to move fast to catch their food. Foxes and wolves run on their toes only. The Arctic fox, which lives in the icy lands around the North Pole, has fur on its feet as well as its legs to help it keep warm.

Elephants are the largest land animal and can weigh up to 6,000kg, so they need strong feet to carry them around. Their feet are big and flat, with expanded pads.

Bats have strong back feet which they use to hang upside down from trees or rock ledges in caves.

The fastest group of animals are those with hooves. Only the very tips of their toenails (the hooves) touch the ground. This makes antelope and deer very fast runners over long distances.

Camels have very unusual feet. Each foot has two toes and two big flat pads. These flat-as-a-pancake feet help them walk on the soft sand of the deserts where they live; if they had hooves they would sink into the sand.

The hippopotamus spends a lot of his time in water. He has four webbed toes on each foot which make him a good swimmer.

YOUR feet
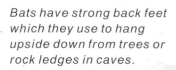

Your feet each have 26 bones. There are five toes – the big toe (hellux) and four smaller ones. The bottom part of your foot is like a cushion, hitting the ground every time you take a step. And you take thousands and thousands of steps every day. Count how many steps you take in a minute. Multiply this by 60. How many steps do you take in an hour? How many in a whole day?

Foot work
Your feet work hard, so look after them. Public enemy number one? Shoes! Try this:
- Take off your shoes and socks. Put your foot flat on a piece of white paper. Draw around it.
- Put the shoe you took off on top. Draw around it in a different colour.
  Are you squeezing your feet into a shape they are not meant to be?

Foot action plan
- Wear shoes that fit.
- Don't wear the same pair of shoes every day.
- Wear clean socks or tights every day.
- Tight socks are as bad as tight shoes. Wear the right size.
- Wash your feet often. Dry carefully between your toes.
- Cut nails straight across.
- Go barefoot in the house.

Feet treat
- Fill a bowl with warm water. Add some slices of lemon.
- Sit with your right foot on your left knee.
- Rub your thumbs in circles over the soles of your feet, heels to toes.
- Tug each toe up gently.
- Repeat for the left foot.
- Soak your feet in the water for 10 minutes. Dry them.

Footercises
In bare feet...
- Spread your toes as wide as you can. Count to three. Relax.
- Roll a tennis ball across the floor under your foot.
- Pick up a pencil with your toes.
- Repeat each footercise three times.

27

MATCHMAKING

by Marion Thompson   illustrations by Kate Simpson

Can you match each animal to its correct description?

1 I eat eucalyptus leaves and belong to a group of mammals called marsupials. I keep my young in a pouch on my body.

2 I live in the Arctic where my thick coat keeps me warm. I am a good swimmer and I eat fish and seals.

3 I am one of the biggest reptiles and I live in rivers in hot countries. I have very sharp teeth.

4 I am a rodent and I live in a lodge. I use my strong teeth to gnaw at small trees to make dams.

5 Most of the time I live under the ground and I am very good at digging.

6 My powerful flippers make me a good swimmer. I live in the sea but come ashore to sunbathe and have my young.

LEAF LINES

by Marion Thompson
illustrations by Kate Simpson

Follow the line from each leaf to find out which tree it comes from.

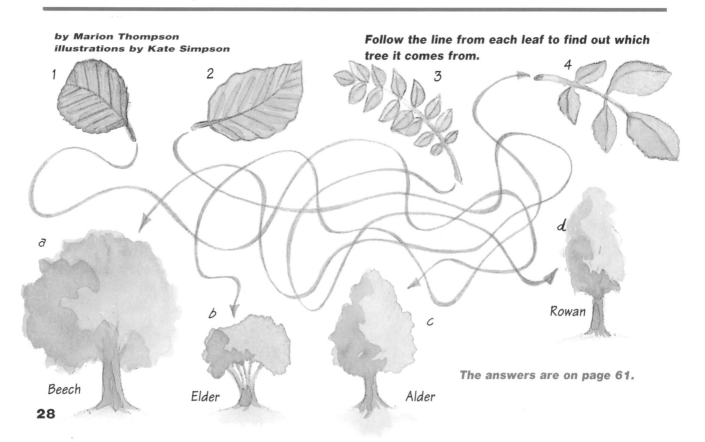

Beech

Elder

Alder

Rowan

The answers are on page 61.

28

Trees have been growing on this planet for about 350 million years! At one time our land was covered with woodlands, before humans began to clear the forests to build settlements and roads.

Depending on the species, a tree takes a long time to reach its full growth; for instance, an oak takes about 150 years, though some conifers are fully grown after about 70 years.

A seed lies in the ground during winter. Then in the spring it sends down roots into the soil to absorb moisture and minerals.

When the roots are established, a shoot appears above ground; the light helps it to produce two 'seed leaves' with a tiny bud between them.

HOW A TREE GROWS

by Gillian Ellis
illustrations by
Helen Herbert

Nourishment is stored in the seed leaves. Soon the bud opens and, as the first pair of true leaves appear, the seed leaves die. The roots strengthen and lengthen. In autumn the leaves drop off the shoot, leaving a 'leader bud' and a 'girdle scar' where the leaves are attached to the stem.

The following spring a new shoot appears from the leader bud, with leaves at its tip, which in turn drop off in the autumn leaving another scar. This process is repeated each year. As the tree grows older it also produces side buds, shoots and leaves, which grow less rapidly than the leader shoot.

During this visible growth, the roots are pushing deeper and deeper into the ground.

All living things need food to survive. The tree produces its own food in its leaves, which contain a green chemical called chlorophyll. The roots supply minerals to the tree, and the action of sunlight, rain and air on the chlorophyll makes the tree's food.

A tree also needs a defence system to protect it against too much sun, rain or harmful diseases. We know this as bark, the tree's outer layer. Underneath the bark there

are several layers, all with a special job to do. Working from the outer layer these are:

● Tubes which supply food from the leaves
● Cambium which grows a new layer of sapwood every year to strengthen and thicken the trunk
● Sapwood containing more tubes which carry water and minerals (sap) from the roots
● Rays which carry food sideways across the trunk
● Heartwood: old, hardened sapwood, now dead, which makes the tree very strong.

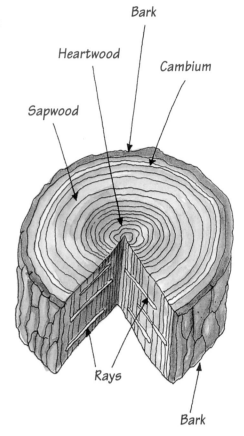

In about its twelfth spring, a tree begins to grow flowers. This is when it is ready to reproduce, with a little help from its friends!

Bees or insects searching the flowers for food carry away pollen which then rubs off on to other flowers of the same species, producing fruit. This is known as 'cross-pollination'. Some trees, mainly conifers and trees with catkins, are pollinated by the wind. The fruit is carried away by birds, animals or humans and the

seeds discarded to take root, or the seed disperses in its own way.

For instance, the sycamore sends its little 'helicopter wings' spinning away on the breeze; horse chestnuts drop their 'conkers', oaks their acorns, beech and hazel their nuts; while conifers open their cones to release seeds which drop to the ground. And there you are! The seeds wait in the ground for the next spring and the growth cycle starts all over again.

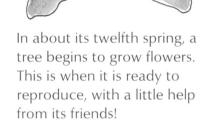

Big oaks from little acorns...

It's possible, with care, to grow a tree from seed, and you'll be helping the environment in the process! Seeds which are usually not too hard to grow are chestnuts, sycamore wings and acorns. Why not try some for starters? Plant more than one, each in its own pot, to give you a greater chance of success.

Here's how to plant an acorn:

- Soak the acorns overnight in warm water.
- Peel away the outer shells if they come off easily, but don't try to cut them off if not.
- Put a layer of small pebbles in a flowerpot for drainage.
- Add soil to about two thirds of the way up the pot and water until it is moist.
- Put in one acorn and add a layer of soil about 2cm deep.
- To keep the soil damp, cover the pot with a plastic bag, tied with string or a rubber band.
- Stand the pot in a light place.
- When a seedling appears, take off the plastic bag.
- Add water to keep the soil moist but not too wet – about twice a week should be enough.
- In the autumn, plant your little tree outside, keeping it in its own soil. Simply tap the base of the pot to loosen the soil and transfer the seedling and soil to a prepared hole.
- Don't forget to keep your tree watered.

31

JELLY
cocktails

Cocktails are mixtures of alcoholic drinks with exotic names which some adults like to drink at parties. But why should grown-ups have all the fun? Conjure up some of these jelly creations and you can have your very own cocktail party!

Sunrise Surprise

You will need:

- 4 glacé cherries
- $\frac{1}{3}$ packet of strawberry flavoured jelly
- $\frac{1}{3}$ packet of orange flavoured jelly
- $\frac{1}{3}$ packet of lemon flavoured jelly
- 4 small tumblers

To make:

Put a glacé cherry in the bottom of each tumbler. Cut the strawberry jelly into cubes using kitchen scissors and put the cubes into a measuring jug. Boil some water in a kettle and carefully pour enough into the jug to cover the jelly cubes. Stir until the cubes are dissolved, then add enough cold water to fill the jug to the 215 millilitres line. Stir and divide the jelly mixture between the four tumblers. Put in the fridge to set.

When the strawberry jelly has set, mix up the orange jelly in the same way and pour a layer into each tumbler. Put in the fridge to set.

When the orange jelly has set, mix up the lemon jelly in the same way and pour a layer into each tumbler. This time when it is set it will be ready to eat.

by Jane Wilson
illustrations by
Anna Hancock

Fairy Foam

You will need:

½ packet lemon flavoured jelly
Approximately 140ml evaporated milk
Sugar flowers
4 jelly dishes

To make:

Cut the jelly into cubes using kitchen scissors and put the cubes into a measuring jug. Boil some water in a kettle and carefully pour enough into the jug to cover the jelly cubes. Stir until the cubes are dissolved then add enough evaporated milk to fill the jug to the 285 millilitres line.

Put the jug in the fridge for about 10 minutes to allow the mixture to cool and just begin to set.

When it is cool pour the mixture into a large mixing bowl and beat it until it is very frothy. Pour into the jelly dishes and put in the fridge to set. When set decorate the fairy foam with sugar flowers.

Slime from the Swamp

You will need:

½ packet lime flavoured jelly
285 ml orange juice
50g jelly animals or monsters
4 jelly dishes

To make:

Cut the jelly into cubes using kitchen scissors and put the cubes into a measuring jug. Boil some water in a kettle and carefully pour enough into the jug to cover the jelly cubes. Stir until the cubes are dissolved, then add enough cold water to fill the jug to the 285 millilitres line.

Stir in the orange juice and put the jug in the fridge. When the mixture is set softly (it will not set really firm because of the extra liquid) stir in the jelly animals and divide the mixture into the jelly dishes. Serve immediately.

ALWAYS ASK A GROWN-UP TO HELP YOU WHEN USING BOILING WATER.

Blacks Fizz

You will need:

3 tablespoons lemon juice
3 tablespoons caster sugar
1 packet blackcurrant flavoured jelly
Approximately 430 ml fizzy water
4 tall wine glasses or 2 tall tumblers
Straws

To make:

Put the bottle of fizzy water in the fridge. Put the lemon juice into a small bowl and the sugar into another small bowl. Dip the top of each glass into the lemon juice and then into the sugar. Put the glasses on one side to dry.

Cut the jelly into cubes using kitchen scissors and put the cubes into a measuring jug. Put the measuring jug into a large bowl. Boil some water in a kettle. Carefully pour about three tablespoons of boiling water into the measuring jug and the rest into the bowl around the outside of the jug. Stir carefully until the jelly is dissolved, then remove the jug from the bowl of water.

Put a straw into each glass.

Take the bottle of fizzy water out of the fridge and pouring slowly down the side of the jug, add enough water to fill the jug to the 570 millilitres line.

Pour the mixture into the glasses and put into the fridge to set.

Snow in summer

You will need:

8 strawberries
$\frac{1}{2}$ packet strawberry flavoured jelly
50g mini marshmallows (or large marshmallows cut into pieces using kitchen scissors)
4 jelly dishes

To make:

Cut the strawberries into slices and divide them between the jelly dishes.

Cut the jelly into cubes using kitchen scissors and put the cubes into a measuring jug. Boil some water in a kettle and carefully pour enough into the jug to cover the jelly cubes. Stir until the cubes are dissolved, then add enough cold water to fill the jug to the 285 millilitres line.

Pour the mixture into the jelly dishes and sprinkle marshmallows over the top. Put in the fridge until set.

EMILY BRINGS GREETINGS FROM KENYA

by Lynda Neilands   illustrations by Jenny Norton

mily's dad had only been home for a few days but already Emily was having problems.

It wasn't that she didn't love her dad. She did. And she missed him terribly when he was away at sea. It was just that now he was back he was so full of plans for things they could do together. Every meal time there was some new idea. At breakfast it had been a visit to her grandmother's, at lunch a trip to the park, and now after tea a game of Monopoly.

Emily had felt mean disappointing him. And then she'd felt cross about being made to feel mean. She wasn't doing anything wrong, after all. She just wanted to spend her spare time her own way – getting to know their new neighbours.

The Sterling family had just moved into the bungalow at the end of the road and Emily thought that Isabel Sterling was wonderful. As well as having Brixton, her pony, and being one of the best young riders in the county, she was really funny and clever and nice. But there was no way their friendship could blossom if Emily spent the two precious weeks before Isabel went back to boarding school playing Monopoly with her dad.

But on reaching home that evening she discovered that there had been a development. Her dad was now entertaining Mrs James in the living-room, while her mum put Sophie to bed. Oh dear! Emily suspected he was about to come up with another unwelcome suggestion.

'Great! I was wondering where you'd got to, Emily.' Mr Martin caught sight of her in the doorway. 'Listen. You're going to love this.'

'This' was an ordinary-looking tape, which he

had just taken out of his travel bag and slotted into the stereo system. 'Here we go.' He pressed the play button. There was a moment of silence. Then, suddenly, a burst of song and rhythm filled the room.

'What does that remind you of?'

'Um… a group of girls singing in a foreign language?' Emily guessed.

'Kenyan Brownies singing in Swahili!' her dad pronounced. 'Our ship was in Mombasa for three days, and I got chatting to this customs official whose daughter was a Brownie. "Mine too," I told him. And before you could say "raise the anchor" I was whisked off to a Brownie meeting to bring greetings from Little Hammington Brownies to their Brownie sisters on the other side of the world.' He saluted proudly.

'That's wonderful, Mike.' Mrs James looked thrilled. 'Are you free to come to our meeting next Friday to play the tape and talk to the Brownies? I'd like them to hear about this as soon as possible.'

'No problem. Emily will lend me a neckerchief and cap – so I'll be able to blend into the background,' Mike Martin grinned.

Mrs James might have been thrilled, but Emily wasn't. In fact she thought her dad's plan to come to Brownies was his worst piece of interference yet.

The problem was that Mrs James had already agreed that Emily could bring a visitor to the meeting next Friday, and Emily had invited Isabel. They'd spent five whole minutes chatting together outside her gate, Isabel holding Brixton's reins, and Emily stroking the pony's smooth jet-black nose. 'We meet in the River Den just beside the lock on the tow path,' Emily had explained.

That meeting had been supposed to cement their friendship, but Emily knew it would be a lot harder to create the right impression if she had her dad tagging along. He'd probably come out with a load of his corny jokes or – worse still – talk about some of the things she had done as a baby. She'd never be able to look Isabel in the face after that!

For the rest of the week she did her best to persuade him to stay at home. When this didn't work, all she could do was try and limit the amount of damage he could do.

'If you come to Brownies, you're to dress properly. You're not to tell silly jokes. And you're to act as if we aren't related…'

Friday night came. Fortunately just as they were about to leave there was a 'phone call.

'No need to travel empty-handed. You can help carry some of that equipment,' Emily's mum called as Emily was about to leave her dad talking and slip out.

By the look of the pile by the door, he was planning to bring half the contents of a souvenir shop to show the Brownies. There was a gourd, a sisal rope, two drums and a large rectangle of brilliantly-coloured cloth which could be wrapped and tucked to make a skirt. Emily picked up the smallest object – and ran.

'Ah, Emily – your dad's coming, isn't he?' smiled Mrs James as the girl arrived alone and panting at the hall.

Emily glanced round quickly to make sure that Isabel wasn't there yet. 'Oh yes, he's coming.' She dropped the tape on the table and retired to her Six corner to welcome

about it, if you like.'

'Good for you!' the Guider nodded and got everyone to sit down in the Ring.

And with that the door was flung open, and someone came dashing into the hall... leaving a muddy trail of footprints across the floor.

'Dad!' Emily ran over to his side. 'Why – you're soaked! Where have you been?'

'In for a little paddle. Nasty current.' He removed a strand of duckweed from the turn-up of his trousers. 'Lucky I had that sisal rope.'

Before she could begin to make sense of this explanation, all the heads in the circle were turning again.

'Do forgive me for interrupting.' A tall elegant stranger had come into the Den and was walking towards Mrs James. 'My name is Frances Sterling. I've come to apologise for my daughter Isabel. Apparently she was to have been here tonight. But would you believe the girl managed to fall into the canal. Oh don't worry! She's perfectly all right. Fortunately someone – a Mr Martin – saw the accident and hauled her out... well... my goodness!'

She spotted Emily's dad. 'We meet again. Of course, I remember now. You were going to speak to your daughter's Brownie Pack, weren't you?'

'That was the general idea,' Mike Martin nodded.

'And this, I take it, is your daughter?' Mrs Sterling turned towards Emily with a smile.

'Shh,' he put his fingers to his lips. 'No-one's meant to know that...'

'Isabel was wondering if she would like to come for tea tomorrow...' Mrs Sterling went on, ignoring the interruption.

Emily flushed pink with pleasure. Here was the perfect opportunity to put things right.

'Like to? I'd love it,' she beamed. 'But could you possibly make it some other time? My dad's just come back from the other side of the world, you see. And we've plans for tomorrow – all day.'

friends and keep as far away from relatives as possible.

The meeting was due to start at six o'clock. By a quarter to seven neither Isabel or Mr Martin had arrived. Whatever could have happened? Isabel's non-appearance was bad enough, but wait till she got her hands on her dad. What did he think he was playing at? When a group of Brownies went to all the trouble of making a tape and sending greetings, the least you could do was deliver them, and not let everyone down.

And then, ten minutes before home time, a horrible thought struck her. Perhaps it was really her fault. Perhaps her dad hadn't turned up because of the way she'd behaved.

Suddenly Emily felt ashamed. 'I'll tell him I'm sorry the minute I get home,' she vowed.

But first she had to do something about those Brownie greetings.

She went over to her Guider. 'Dad's 'phone call must have taken longer than expected,' she said. 'But I could play the tape and explain

Kenyan PUZZLES

by Jane Wilson   illustrations by Jenny Norton and Sue Cony

Jambo! That means hello in Swahili, one of the main languages used in my country of Kenya. English is the other main language, but many different languages are spoken and at Brownies we each learn to say our Promise, which is very like yours, in the language we speak at home. When we make our Promise we are given a woggle with a picture of a bird on it. We use this to fasten our yellow neckerchief which we wear with a light brown dress. We meet in a Brownie Flock run by Wise Bird.

Kenya is on the east coast of Africa, right on the equator, so it is always hot here, although we have some very high mountains which are capped with snow. The country takes its name from Mount Kenya, our highest mountain, whose native name means white mountain. These pages will help you to learn a little more about my country. Kwaheri – goodbye.

We have many animals in Kenya and we do our best to protect them. Over 54,000 square kilometres of the country is protected in reserves and national parks. If you ever come to Kenya you might go on 'safari', a Swahili word meaning journey, through one of our national parks. You would have to be as quiet and as still as possible, as many of the animals are very shy. There are six Kenyan animals – a lion, an elephant, a hippopotamus, a leopard, a zebra and a giraffe – hiding in this picture. Can you spot them?

The people of Kenya originate from over 40 African tribes, and our national flag shows a shield and two crossed spears to remind us of our past. Kenya is largely a rural country with four fifths of the population living in villages, growing food and keeping animals to eat and to sell. The traditional dwelling is a round hut with a thatched roof, for it was believed that if there were no corners evil spirits could not hide in the hut. Now, however, rectangular huts with corrugated tin roofs are increasingly common.

Although people are adapting to modern ways, tribal customs are kept alive, especially in the music. Kenyans love dancing, singing and playing instruments. Long drums from hollow logs covered with hide are held between the legs and played with both hands. They were once used to send messages over distances of up to 12 kilometres. Here is a man of the Chuka sub-tribe who are famed for their drumming. You will get a better idea of what he looks like if you colour him in. His head-dress is made from the black and white skin of the colobus monkey and his skirt of dried grasses. The jewellery around his neck is of many brilliant colours, as are the patterns on his drum.

Our warm weather enables many crops to be grown. Tea and coffee are two of the things which Kenya exports to the rest of the world. We like to drink tea, or chai as we call it, but you would find it quite different to your drink. To make it we put milk, water, tea leaves and lots of sugar all together in a kettle and bring them to the boil, then drink it very hot. Here are pictures of six fruits which are grown in Kenya, but their names have got jumbled up. Can you unscramble the letters and join the right name to the right fruit? You will find the answers on page 61.

LEAPPINEP _ _ _ _ _ _ _ _ _

NAABAN _ _ _ _ _ _

VOODACA _ _ _ _ _ _ _

GAMNO _ _ _ _ _

SOPSAIN TRIFU _ _ _ _ _ _ _ _ _ _ _

VAUGA _ _ _ _ _

Creature crossword

by Marion Thompson

This year's competition is for those of you who enjoy crosswords.

Solve the clues and fit your answers into the correct places in the grid. When you've done them all, rearrange the letters in the coloured squares to make the name of another animal.

Then, send the name of the animal, your name, age and address and the titles of the three things you liked best in this year's Brownie Annual on a postcard to:

The Brownie Annual 1995
The Guide Association
17-19 Buckingham Palace Road
London SW1W 0PT

The five lucky winners will receive one of these special ELEFRIENDS t-shirts.

Photo: Dave Coomber

The closing date for entries is 31 January 1995.

The winners will be notified by post and the editor's decision is final.

ACROSS

1 This tusky animal carries its own trunk. (8)
5 Paddington, Rupert or Pooh. (4)
7 As strong as an ____. (2)
8 The Queen owns this breed of dog. (5)
10 This snake is good at sums. (5)
12 A flying mammal. (3)
13 The king of the beasts. (4)
14 A tiny insect. (3)
16 Similar to a butterfly. (4)
21 A male sheep. (3)
22 It lives in a set. (6)
23 It grows into a frog. (7)
24 Black Beauty was one. (5)
26 There was one called Tarka. (5)
28 An extinct bird. (4)
29 It spins a web. (6)
30 An expensive animal? (4)

DOWN

2 Can this animal change its spots? (7)
3 It lives in a sty. (3)
4 He raced against the hare. (8)
6 The first animal in the dictionary. (8)
9 A creepy-crawly with six legs. (6)
11 Will it desert a sinking ship? (3)
15 This animal doesn't play fair. (7)
17 It has eight 'arms'. (7)
18 A clucking bird. (3)
19 An Australian jumper? (8)
20 An animal you can cross on. (5)
22 It might sting you. (3)
25 Jersey, Guernsey or Friesian. (3)
27 A female sheep. (3)

THE BORN FREE FOUNDATION

Do you love animals? Do you know about the Born Free Foundation?

It's a very animal-friendly charity working to protect wildlife with a special Junior Club.

Some of its work which you might have heard of includes ELEFRIENDS, the Elephant Protection Group working to give the elephant a safe future, Operation Wolf, which runs a special sanctuary to help rescued and injured Iberian wolves (who aren't big and bad at all!) in Portugal, and Zoo Check, which looks at the issues involved in keeping animals in captivity. It also helps protect rhinos, chimps and dolphins, so whatever your favourite animal is, the Born Free Foundation is doing something to help it.

There are also amazing 'adoption' schemes which really do make you part of the wildlife family. It's a great present and you could find yourself an adopted sister (or brother) to a wolf, a chimpanzee or a whole family of elephants!

Junior members receive their own newsletter, *Trumpet*, three times a year, details of special wild gear to wear, plus all the fun of Wildlife Week (a chance to go really wild) in October. For more information on how you can join in, please send a stamped addressed envelope to: The Born Free Foundation/Guides, Coldharbour, Dorking, Surrey RH5 6HA.

AS SAFE AS HOUSES?

by Ann Moynihan   illustrations by Anna King

Have you ever heard the saying 'As safe as houses'? It sounds nice, doesn't it – comforting, as though nothing could harm you if you were at home. But do you know where most accidents happen? Not on the road, not at school – but in ordinary houses and flats where people are living. Accidents happen all the time, and many people are hurt enough to have to go to hospital.

But don't despair. When you made your Promise as a Brownie you said you'd do your best to keep that Promise everywhere, and that includes when you are at home. And there's a very special way you can do that – by helping to make your home (and your school and Pack meeting place!) a safe place for other people to be in.

On these pages you can see different places, each with a number of things about them which could cause accidents – that is, if there wasn't a Brownie about to put them right! Cover up the answers at the bottom of the page and see if you can spot the dangers. Then check your answers and see what a Brownie would do. When you have finished, go round your own home and find out whether it is 'as safe as houses'.

ANSWERS

In the garden
What would a Brownie do? Make sure the children weren't left on their own near the pond, or allowed to eat berries; put away garden tools and chemicals in a safe place, like the garden shed.

In the hall and on the stairs
What would a Brownie do? Fasten the safety gate, put bags and toys in their proper places, and ask an adult to fit safety film or toughened glass to the door.

In the living room
What would a Brownie do? Put the drinks somewhere higher up, out of reach of the child, and put the fireguard in front of the fire. (Did you know it is illegal to leave a child under 12, or 7 in Scotland, on its own with an unguarded fire?) Put the matches and cigarettes away. Ask an adult to check the wiring of the plugs and if possible add an extra socket to avoid the risk of fire.

In the kitchen
What would a Brownie do? Quickly take the knife from the baby and put it away, then close the cupboard door; turn the pan handles away from the stove edge and take the children out of the kitchen to play somewhere else. The iron flex won't hurt anyone as there is no one to pull it!

In the bedroom
What would a Brownie do? Close the window and move the chair away from it. Take the scissors from one child and put them away. Ask an adult to fit a socket cover so that children cannot stick fingers (or other objects) into the socket holes. Move the other child away from the door to play so that she doesn't trap her fingers. Ask an adult if you can help put the boxes on the wardrobe somewhere safer, or to stack them more safely.*

In the bathroom
What would a Brownie do? Stay with the child until an adult came back (did you know that a child can drown in less than 4cm of water?) and mop up the water on the floor. Shut away the medicines in the bathroom cupboard and ask an adult to fit a safe and secure cupboard for medicines and other dangerous chemicals such as bleach and toilet cleaner.*

Girls living hundreds of years ago had to make the most of the games and puzzles they played with. There were no computer games for them. But one of those puzzles is as much fun now as it was in ancient times.

The tangram first puzzled Chinese children, and is a little bit like a jigsaw. But there is only one way to complete a jigsaw – and hundreds of ways to complete a tangram! Why not make one, and try to solve the mystery of the seven tans?

Tricky, teasing...
TANGRAMS

by Libby Coolson
illustrations by Frances Lloyd

You will need:

A piece of card (cereal packets are good) or paper
Ruler
Pencil
Coloured crayons or felt tipped pens
Safety scissors

1 Using a pencil and ruler, draw a 12cm square.
2 Draw three lines across the square and three lines down the square. The lines must be 3cm apart. Count the little squares – you should have 16.
3 Copy the diagram and draw five thick black lines in your tangram square.
4 The thick lines make seven shapes. Colour each one like the diagram.
5 Cut along the thick lines. You will now have seven pieces of card. These are called tans.

The tangram puzzle

Mix up the tans. Keep them coloured side up. Now all you have to do is fit them together again to make the tangram square. This is not as easy as it looks!

Tangram pictures

Can you make these
tangram shadow pictures?
You must use all seven
tans for each one, and the
pieces must not overlap.

The tangram challenge

- Can you make tangram
  pictures of your own?
  Remember to use all seven
  tans.
- Make a tiny tangram for a
  travel or holiday puzzle. Draw
  it on an 8cm square of
  cardboard.
- Make a big tangram to solve
  as a Pack activity. Draw a big
  60cm or 80cm square on a
  cardboard packing box.
- Make bigger or smaller
  tangrams. Remember that
  each side of the square must
  always divide into four.

Did you make the
tangram
pictures? If you
need some help,
look on page 61.

Upon the Snail

by John Bunyan
illustration by Guy Parker-Rees

She goes but softly, but she goeth sure;
She stumbles not as stronger creatures do:
Her journey's shorter, so she may endure
Better than they which do much further go.

She makes no noise, but stilly seizeth on
The flower or herb appointed for her food,
The which she quietly doth feed upon,
While others range, and gare,* but find no good.

And though she doth but very softly go,
However 'tis not fast, nor slow, but sure;
And certainly they that do travel so,
The prize they do aim at, they do procure.

* Gare: stare about.

AUNT ROSE'S SPECIAL CAKE

by Heather Gorst
illustrations by Kate Simpson

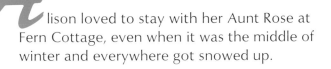

Alison loved to stay with her Aunt Rose at Fern Cottage, even when it was the middle of winter and everywhere got snowed up.

'What shall we do today?' she asked as she helped Aunt Rose to clear the breakfast things away.

'I thought we might make a rather special kind of cake,' said Aunt Rose. 'Would you like to lend a Brownie hand?'

'Yes, please,' said Alison at once. 'I love running my finger round the bowl afterwards and licking it.'

Aunt Rose gave her a funny look and began to put out some chopped bacon rind, a handful of currants, a few cooked potatoes, a whole pile of cake crumbs and some brown bread plus a handful of seeds and last of all a lump of fat. Alison looked on in amazement. Surely they couldn't be having such a cake for tea – could they?

'I wish you could see your face, Alison!' Aunt Rose burst out laughing. 'Haven't you ever made a cake for the birds?'

Alison laughed too. 'I should have guessed! I like to feed the birds at home but I've never made a cake for them before. Do show me how.'

First of all Aunt Rose heaped all the nuts, currants and other ingredients into a large basin. Then she melted the fat and poured it over the mixture and left it to set.

'Now what else do we need besides some peanuts and over-ripe fruit?' She looked expectantly at Alison.

47

'Water,' said Alison promptly.

'Good girl. So many people forget that the birds need a drink and that it's vital for them to bathe daily and keep their feathers in good order, especially when it's cold weather. Now, where did I put the nightlights?'

'On the shelf behind you,' said a puzzled Alison. She wondered why the birds needed nightlights.

When the cake had set firmly enough, Aunt Rose and Alison pulled on their wellingtons and crunched through the frosty snow to the bird-table. The cold snapped at their fingers and turned their noses pink.

The cake was turned out onto the table carefully and broken into large chunks. Aunt Rose found a couple of bricks, swept away some of the snow and balanced a dish of water on the bricks. Then she placed a lighted nightlight underneath.

'Now I understand!' exclaimed Alison. 'The nightlight is to keep the water from freezing.'

Then Aunt Rose hung a container full of peanuts on a nearby branch, and told Alison briskly not to put all the food on the bird-table but to scatter some of it on the ground and to roll a couple of apples under the hedge.

'But the food will get mushy in the snow,' objected Alison.

'Ah, but you must remember that some birds, like the blackbirds and thrushes, prefer to feed on the ground and don't come so readily to the bird-table.'

When they got back to the house they made some hot chocolate and sipped it sitting by the window. They didn't have to wait for long. The first visitor was a bright-eyed robin followed by a score of noisy sparrows and then the blue-tits found the peanuts and had a feast.

'Look,' Aunt Rose nudged Alison suddenly. 'There is a grey squirrel after the nuts.'

'I thought squirrels slept through the winter,' whispered Alison.

'You're thinking of red squirrels; the greys don't hibernate.'

'I hope he doesn't steal all the nuts, the tits need them,' said Alison and wondered if she should shoo him away.

'No, the winter is hard for him too.' Aunt Rose watched the busy crowd outside the window. 'We can put some more out later. Ideally food should be put out in the morning, since the birds need their breakfast the same as we do, and a feed at night helps them to survive the cold. I do believe it's snowing again. You might be able to go tobogganing tomorrow, Alison.'

'Good,' said Alison, 'but can we make another bird cake first?'

* * *

Perhaps you would like to make Aunt Rose's Special Cake for the birds in your garden? Here is the recipe she used when showing Alison how to make it.

You will need:

25g currants
110g mixed wild bird seed
350g cooked potatoes, cubed
75g stale cake crumbs
75g wholemeal breadcrumbs
small quantity of chopped bacon rind
110g fat
75g unsalted peanuts

First of all put some newspaper under a large bowl to catch any bits. Then mix all the ingredients, except the fat, in the basin. You can do this with a spoon or have a lovely messy time mixing it with your hands! Now ask a grown-up to melt the fat for you as, if you should have an accident, spilt hot fat can be very painful. You can use plain lard, but good old-fashioned suet or dripping from the butcher is much better. Pour the melted fat over all the ingredients and leave the mixture to set. When the cake is quite firm, turn it out and either divide it into large chunks as Aunt Rose did or hang it up in a net like a ball of fat. The birds will have a great time tucking into their treat and you will have a wonderful time watching them!

Don't worry if you haven't got all the ingredients listed. You can still make a very satisfactory cake from the birds' point of view using other ingredients.

No currants? Sultanas are equally good or a small eating apple, cut into bite-sized pieces, will make a good substitute. If you want to make a bigger cake add any left-over uncooked pastry or cooked pasta and an extra handful of unsalted peanuts – not the salted variety as salt is bad for birds. Canary seeds or sunflower seeds are all good extras to put in your cake. Not enough breadcrumbs? Make some by taking 75g of wholemeal flour and 25g margarine and rubbing them together until the mixture is nice and crumbly. Don't use white bread for crumbs, as many bird experts say the small birds can't digest it, so stick to wholemeal. No cake left? Never mind – use the broken biscuits from the bottom of the biscuit tin. They are rich in oil and fat and are excellent for birds who need to store up fat against the cold.

Have fun making your bird cake!

Bird Search

by Marion Thompson
illustrations by
Diana Catchpole

The 40 birds listed on the right can all be found in the word square – vertically, horizontally or diagonally. How many can you find?

Albatross	Dunnock	Magpie	Rook
Barn Owl	Eagle	Nightingale	Skylark
Blackbird	Gannet	Partridge	Sparrow
Blue-tit	Goldfinch	Pelican	Starling
Chaffinch	Goose	Penguin	Swallow
Crow	Heron	Pigeon	Swift
Cuckoo	Jackdaw	Puffin	Thrush
Curlew	Jay	Raven	Toucan
Dove	Kestrel	Redstart	Wren
Duck	Kingfisher	Robin	Yellowhammer

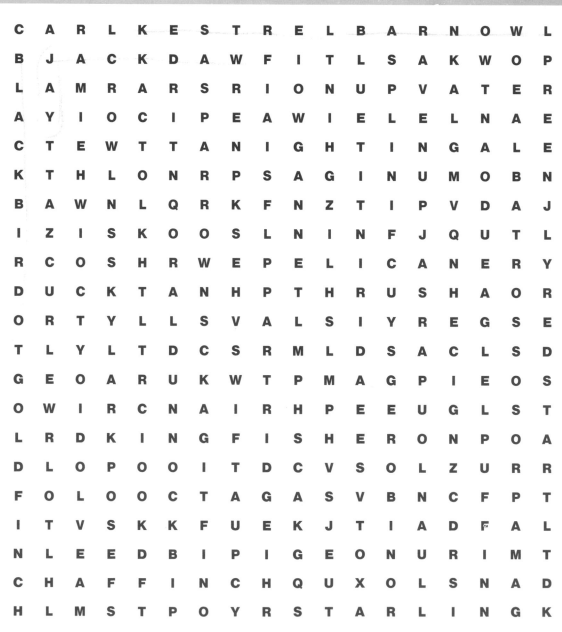

```
C A R L K E S T R E L B A R N O W L
B J A C K D A W F I T L S A K W O P
L A M R A R S R I O N U P V A T E R
A Y I O C I P E A W I E L E L N A E
C T E W T T A N I G H T I N G A L E
K T H L O N R P S A G I N U M O B N
B A W N L Q R K F N Z T I P V D A J
I Z I S K O O S L N I N F J Q U T L
R C O S H R W E P E L I C A N E R Y
D U C K T A N H P T H R U S H A O R
O R T Y L L S V A L S I Y R E G S E
T L Y L T D C S R M L D S A C L S D
G E O A R U K W T P M A G P I E O S
O W I R C N A I R H P E E U G L S T
L R D K I N G F I S H E R O N P O A
D L O P O O I T D C V S O L Z U R R
F O L O O C T A G A S V B N C F P T
I T V S K K F U E K J T I A D F A L
N L E E D B I P I G E O N U R I M T
C H A F F I N C H Q U X O L S N A D
H L M S T P O Y R S T A R L I N G K
```

Imagine yourself at a grand dance a hundred years ago. The room is full of people and heated by a big roaring fire. You are wearing a thick, tightly fitting dress, layers of petticoats, and thick underwear laced tight. How do you keep cool? With a fan, an important part of every young lady's wardrobe.

fanTASIA!

by Brenda Apsley
illustrations by
Jacky Rough

Fans have been used for at least 5,000 years. Early fans were a stick with a piece of fabric or paper on top – one made of ivory and ostrich feathers was found in Tutankhamun's tomb in Egypt.

Folding fans made of thin pieces – 'sticks' – and a folded top part appeared around 1500. Queen Elizabeth I, who lived from 1533 to 1603, made them popular in Britain. At that time fans were also used for wafting flies and bad smells away!

Fans were part of fashion, chosen with as much care as clothes. The sticks were made of wood (sometimes covered in gold), ivory or mother of pearl. The tops were made of paper, silk or lace. Some were painted, or you could buy plain paper ones to paint yourself.

One fan made around 1900 opened up into a full circle of peacock feathers. Another made of swansdown had a stuffed swan in the middle. Poor birds!

Fans went out of fashion after the Second World War, which ended in 1945, though cheap paper ones were still given free to advertise hotels and shops. They are still used in Spain though – perhaps you have seen them on holiday?

If you would like to see lots of fans of all shapes and sizes, why not visit the Fan Museum in Greenwich, London? It is the only fan museum in the world, and has more than 2,000 fans. Ring 081 858 7879 to find out opening times.

Folded Fan

To make a folded fan you will need:
2 pieces of A4 (30x21cm) paper
Pencil
Ruler
Narrow sticky tape

1 Using sticky tape join the pieces of paper along the 21cm edges. Your paper is now 60x21cm.
2 Using a pencil and ruler, draw 19 lines across the paper, 3cm apart.

3 On a flat surface, make a fold along line 1. Fold up and away from you. Make the fold as straight as you can. Run your finger along the fold to create a firm crease.
4 Turn the paper over. Fold along line 2. Turn over.
5 Keep on folding and turning until you get to the end of the paper.
6 Wrap a 9-10cm piece of sticky tape around one end of the paper.
7 Holding the taped end, pull the folds apart gently. That's it!

1 & 2

60cm

Line 1
Line 2

Tape

Line 19

21cm

side view

5

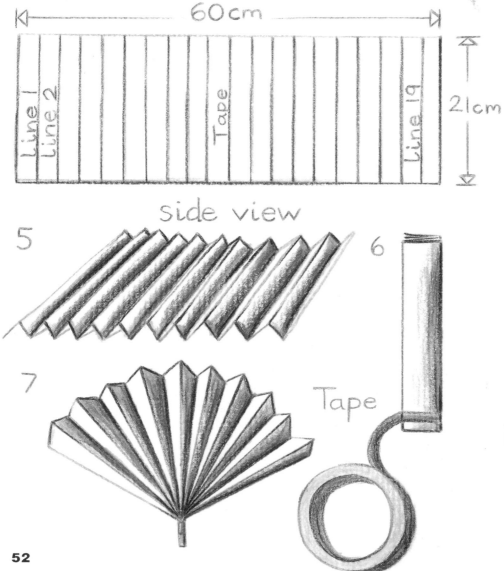

7

6

Tape

3 & 4

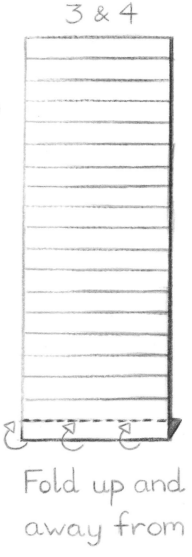

Fold up and away from you

52

Picture Fan

1 Draw a picture on one side of the paper using paints, felt-tipped pens or coloured pencils. Craft paper is best for this. A rainbow over green fields is a good design to try.
2 Leave to dry.
3 Draw lines on the BACK of your picture. Fold as before, and tape the end.

- **Young ladies who lived hundreds of years ago used to paint their own fans.**
- **Send a 'birthday' fan. Paint a picture and write your message on the paper before folding it. Put a paper clip to hold the top edges and for a friend to open.**

Wall Fan

1 Make a fan using a piece of scrap wallpaper 50x150cm. You could use patterned wallpaper, or paint a picture or design on the blank side.
2 Make folds 5cm apart, and wrap sticky tape around one end.
3 Put a sticky tab or Blu-tak on each top side and put the fan on your bedroom wall.

Cut-out Fan

1 Make a 60x21cm fan, tape one end but do not open out the fan.
2 Using safety scissors, make little snips along one long edge of the folded paper.
3 Make tiny zig-zag snips along the top edge. Open out the fan.

- **On one side of the fan you could tape pieces of coloured paper or tissue over the cut-out shapes.**
- **A black fan with red, blue and yellow tissue makes a fan like a stained glass window.**

Brooch fan

1 Cut out a piece of patterned gift paper 12x4cm.
2 Draw lines 1cm apart and fold the fan. These folds are tiny, so you might have to practise! Tape one end.
3 Cut out a 2cm square of card.
4 Tape a tiny gold safety pin to the card.
5 Glue the card to the back of the fan.
6 Pin the fan brooch to your clothes.

- **Add a loop and hang these tiny fans from the Christmas tree.**

Fishy fan

1 Cut out a 60x20cm piece of bright blue craft paper.
2 Tear yellow and gold paper into simple fish shapes. Draw in eyes.
3 Tear green paper into long pieces of seaweed.
4 Tear pink and white paper into shell shapes.
5 Glue the torn paper shapes to the blue paper to make an underwater scene.
6 You could glue on sequin or bead 'bubbles' if you like.
7 Draw lines on the back, then fold and tape the fan as before.

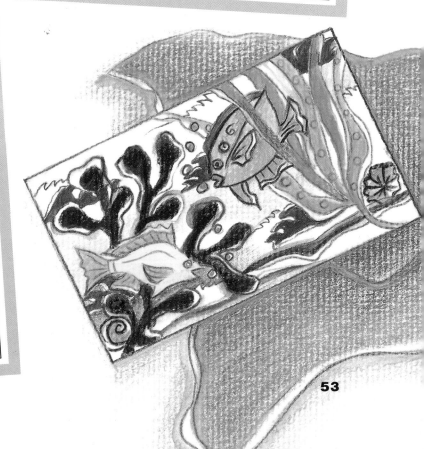

Playdays!

Photographs by Lucy Drew

Recipe for happy faces: let six Brownies loose in the Bethnal Green Museum of Childhood!

The museum has anything and everything that children long ago would have loved – rocking horses, toy soldiers, books, games, dolls and huge dolls' houses, puppet shows and a case full of model sheep that sing when you press a button! You can even play with some of the toys. Or take an adult and see if they find an old favourite! The museum is in Cambridge Heath Road, London E2. Telephone 081 980 2415 for details.

Come and look at this one!

Toys for sale!

Roll up, roll up, for all the fun of the fair!

A girl's best friend

There's always something new just around the corner

Whoever said museums were boring?

Tired but happy

DYNAMIC TOYS

With thanks to the Bethnal Green Museum of Childhood and Katy Benneworth, Lucy Briois, Rebecca Clarke, Kerrie Gale, Eloise Gale, Sian Pulyk and Guider Alison Hetherington of the 4th Hayes Pack.

Look at those great big grins!

HANGING GARDENS

by Gill Pawley
illustrations by Cheryl Tarbuck

You will need:

- An empty round margarine tub or ice-cream carton
- Scissors
- 240cm string
- Compost or soil
- Flowers

In summer time, one of the prettiest sights in a garden is a hanging basket full of beautiful flowers. If a basket is hung high up on a wall or fence, bees and butterflies are attracted to it as well.

You can make your own hanging basket from a margarine or ice-cream carton (or, indeed, any other lightweight plastic container). One of the most important things to think about is the size – you will want your container to be large enough for several plants to create a nice effect. This may mean that you may have to hunt around a bit to get the right size of tub, or ask your family and friends for help.

Once you have found your ideal tub, give it a really good clean inside and out. This is especially important if your tub has had greasy margarine in it. Do not worry too much about what is on the outside of the container. Hopefully, your plants will grow over the sides and cover any writing or pictures.

What next?

You will need to make holes in your container, through which you will thread string to hang up the basket. It is most important to get the help of an adult, because the plastic will probably be quite hard and you could easily hurt yourself if you attempted this on your own.

Ask your adult helper to make three small holes at regular intervals, just below the rim of the carton. The holes need to be large enough for the string to thread through.

Next cut three pieces of string, each 80cm long. Thread each piece of string through one of the holes, from the inside of the pot outwards. Then tie a knot at the end of the string inside the container.

When you have threaded all three strings, join them all together and tie with a knot.

This large knot needs to be very secure, because the string has to hold the weight of the container plus some soil and the flowers.

Hang on!

Now that you have a hanging container, do you know where you will hang it? Ideally you need a hook or a nail from which to hang the basket. This is so that the container can look its best, with lots of flowers cascading over the sides.

Try to make sure that your hanging basket hangs well away from the wall or fence, otherwise your plants will not grow properly.

You can now start to think about planting your hanging basket. The first thing to do is to put some plastic, such as a plastic bag or bin liner, in the bottom of the basket (this helps to keep the soil in the basket moist).

Next, put the compost or soil into the container. Make sure that you press down the compost or soil firmly, so that the plants will develop strong, healthy roots. Then put a small amount of water in and leave for at least one day so that the compost or soil settles.

What to plant

Some plants are particularly good in hanging baskets. You will want to try to have a few plants that will trail over the side of the tub such as ivy and lobelia. Ask an adult to help you with this because you may need to buy the plants. Make sure that the trailing plants are put right at the edge of the pots so that they will grow over the side.

Pansies, bizzy lizzies and petunias will all grow well in the middle of the container and look very pretty. See if you can get cuttings from other gardeners or perhaps grow some plants from seed.

When you start to plant, put the tallest plant in the centre of the basket.

Do not plant the flowers too close together because, as they grow, the plants will quickly fill the container.

It is very important that you water your hanging basket a lot. In hot weather, you may have to water the flowers every day. Remember to remove any dead flowers as well. In this way you will have a stunning display all summer long.

①

holes — 3 → 7° Knot end

3 × 80 cms pieces of string

After an adult has made 3 holes, thread each piece of string through and secure with Knot inside

② Knot strongly.

fill with compost and add a little water

piece of plastic bag or bin liner

Ideal flowers for hanging baskets

- Trailing lobelia
- Trailing ivy
- Geraniums
- Petunias
- Pansies
- Bizzy lizzies

Petunias   ivy   geranium   Bizzy Lizzies   Pansies   lobelia

YOU DON'T HAVE TO GO TO THE JUNGLE!

by Ann Moynihan
illustrations by
Jan Lewis

One of the badge tests for the first Guides and Scouts was to 'stalk' an animal or bird – that is, creep up on it like a hunter very carefully and quietly. Unlike a hunter, though, the Guides and Scouts didn't catch or kill it, but watched how it behaved – how it moved, what it ate, whether it was alone or with a group of other animals, how it kept a look-out for danger. Nowadays, we have so many television programmes which use cameras with special lenses to take us right up to animals all over the world that you might think you needn't stir from your living-room to see wildlife! But watching wild animals and birds is still fun, and you can do it right where you are – in the garden, in the park, on Pack Holiday, or at the beach.

Look around your garden or a nearby park – there may be grey squirrels looking for food, or birds 'bathing' themselves in the dust. Try to get closer, walking slowly, with no sudden movements, and pause a lot, so that the animal or bird can get used to you. Don't worry if it spots you – just stand still. If it thinks you're not a danger it will let you get quite close before it runs away. How close can you get? Don't stalk just one creature for ages – it needs to feed!

Look carefully at your creature:

- what size is it?
- is it furry, feathery, scaly, or what?
- what sort of feet does it have?
- how does it feed? Does it have 'hands' or use its teeth?

How does your animal behave? How does it:

- stand?
- look around?
- eat?
- get about: slowly or quickly?

If you're lucky enough to live near a nature reserve there will probably be special hides, where you can look out at animals or birds without them knowing you're there. You can find out where your nearest nature reserve is from your local library or Tourist Information Centre. The best person to tell you about the wildlife at the reserve is the warden – why not ask your Guider to write to her or him and ask if a small group of you can visit? The warden may also be able to lend you binoculars and books to help you identify birds and animals.

You can also watch birds through your window – look out for different kinds. Borrow a reference book from the library and make a checklist of the birds you see. Watch how different birds fly and feed, and what kinds of food they like best. Do they fight amongst themselves? If there aren't many cats where you live, you could put out food to encourage birds to visit. See pages 48 and 49 for information on food for birds.

It's easier to find insects and you don't have to stalk them! Every home has spiders – don't scream, they won't hurt you! When you find a spider, look carefully at it – count its legs, look at its eyes (on stalks!) and at any markings it has on its body. You could make a collection of drawings of spiders you find in your house. Look at spiders' webs, and see how carefully they are woven. Remember that spiders are really our friends, because they catch flies which spread germs and diseases.

If you have a garden you might find ladybirds. These are also our friends – they eat greenfly and other insects which damage plants by sucking the sap out of leaves and stalks. Use a magnifying glass to look at the spots on a ladybird's back, and see how it flies off when it is startled. Look under stones and wood to find woodlice, which look like tiny armadillos. Most gardens also have plenty of slugs and snails, which are amazing creatures, although they are not the gardener's friend, because some types eat plants – especially sweet, crunchy lettuces and young plant shoots. Snails and many slugs come in lots of shapes and sizes, some with different patterned shells, all with stalks on their heads – the top two for 'seeing' with (they do this by sensing light and dark), the lower two for sensing food. They leave a slimy trail behind them, and if you put a snail on a sheet of glass you can watch how its single foot moves it along.

In your local area there may be a WATCH group for children who want to help animals and care about the environment. WATCH groups often organise events for children, such as bumblebee walks, visits to nature reserves and conservation projects. Every year there is a special national project for WATCH members – for example, surveying rivers and water wildlife or looking at people's attitudes to bats and otters ('battitudes' and 'ottertudes'!). A Brownie Pack can join WATCH as a group member, or you could join on your own. Write to WATCH (address below) for details.

Here are some of the different organisations for children who are interested in watching and conserving wild animals and birds:

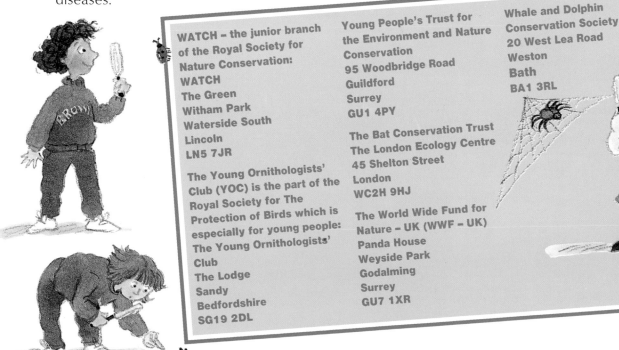

WATCH – the junior branch of the Royal Society for Nature Conservation:
WATCH
The Green
Witham Park
Waterside South
Lincoln
LN5 7JR

The Young Ornithologists' Club (YOC) is the part of the Royal Society for The Protection of Birds which is especially for young people:
The Young Ornithologists' Club
The Lodge
Sandy
Bedfordshire
SG19 2DL

Young People's Trust for the Environment and Nature Conservation
95 Woodbridge Road
Guildford
Surrey
GU1 4PY

The Bat Conservation Trust
The London Ecology Centre
45 Shelton Street
London
WC2H 9HJ

The World Wide Fund for Nature – UK (WWF – UK)
Panda House
Weyside Park
Godalming
Surrey
GU7 1XR

Whale and Dolphin Conservation Society
20 West Lea Road
Weston
Bath
BA1 3RL

MAY 1993   £1.00

Brownie
Plus... Rainbow Guide Extra

Super Brownie and the M...

fun foo

Spring is coming at last after
the winter months. Eggs are t...
symbols of s...

If you want exciting activities, crafty ideas, super stories and fabulous features, make sure you get a copy of BROWNIE - the monthly magazine just for Brownies like you.

Each month there's a thrilling adventure for Super Brownie and her friends, a story about Freda the elephant and lots of features to help you with badge work.

There are also fun and easy recipes, experiments to try, puzzles to solve, games to play, competitions to enter and lots of information on Brownies around the world.

You can even send in your own letters, poems, prayers and photographs, which may get printed on the Pinboard pages, or apply for a Brownie pen-pal. So write and let us know what you and your Pack have been up to recently.

But that's not all! As well as 32 pages of Brownie material, there is also an eight-page section specially for Rainbows. So if you have a younger sister who's a Rainbow you can pull out this middle section and give it to her.

The section also has lots of things to make and do, including crafts, cookery and puzzles. And there's space for Rainbow letters and photos too.

So don't miss out. Join in the fun and order your copy now!

---

6 BOX

Ideas for Sixes to try together.

RAINBOW FLOWERS

Below are the jumbled up names of flowers. Can you work out what they are? Clue: the colour of each flower comes in the same order as the colours of the rainbow, but the middle rainbow colour is missing. Can you think why?

1 MIAEGRNU
2 DOIAMRGL
3 URTUBTECP
4 OETGOFREMNT
5 STMLCEAI
6 TLIVOE

PATCHWORK PAIR UP

Collect 30 or more pieces of scrap fabric at least 15cm square. Fold each piece in half and cut an irregular shape through the double thickness. Sort pieces into two piles — one for the cut-outs, the other for the remaining fabric. Scatter one pile around the room, then spread the other pile on a table.

At a signal, each Brownie chooses one piece of fabric f... and goes to find its twin. When she has a pair, she may ta... piece from the table. The Brownie with the most pairs at t...

It makes it harder if you have several pairs of the same material, but in different shapes.

HELICOPTER SEEDS

The seeds of some trees, such as sycamore and maple, spin like a helicopter as they fall to the ground.

Try making your own helicopter seed.

Cut this shape out of thin card and then cut along the dotted lines, A and B.

Fold along the lo... make the 'blades' helicopter.

Stick a small blob on the bottom of th...

If each member makes a helicopter drop them at the s... and see which one... ground first.

GROWING UP

The sentences below are a bit strange! Can your Six match up the pairs correctly?

A tadpole grows into a swan.
A chick grows into a frog.
A cygnet grows into a butterfly.
A caterpillar grows into a hen.

FRUIT SE...

There are ten ...
in this square ...
them all?

PEARKSB'
MEHBOIAU
ITAPRRNI
WAPCGRAP
JFPSHENN
DCLKAMAN
PIETRAPI

The answers are...

3

---

answers to puzzles

Puzzle time, page 13

Petal poser
1 snowdrop; 2 marigold;
3 primrose; 4 daffodil.

Seed hunt

Canadian puzzles, page 22

The place names are: *Medicine Hat; Yellowknife; Moose Jaw; York Factory; Big Salmon; Rainy River and Whitehorse.*

D	O	G	S	L	E	D	D	I	N	G
I	F	E	S	S	O	R	C	A	L	R
O	O	I	S	E	T	H	A	T	L	I
W	O	L	L	D	O	C	M	Y	A	B
E	T	G	T	T	O	A	D	O	B	M
G	B	N	D	U	T	N	Y	T	T	O
N	A	I	C	E	H	O	C	K	E	Y
I	L	H	D	T	O	E	S	E	K	R
D	L	S	E	G	N	I	I	K	S	T
I	H	I	E	Q	U	N	E	E	A	N
R	A	F	T	I	N	G	A	N	B	D

More puzzles, page 28

Leaf lines
1 = c; 2 = a; 3 = d; 4 = b.

Matchmaking

1c – koala	4b – beaver
2e – polar bear	5a – mole
3f – crocodile	6d – seal

Kenyan puzzles, page 38

Pineapple    Mango

Banana   Passion fruit

Avocado   Guava

Tricky, teasing... tangrams, page 45

The house   The eagle

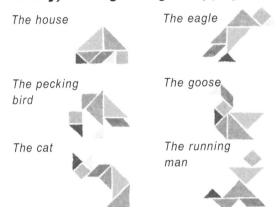

The pecking bird   The goose

The cat   The running man

Bird search, page 50

C	A	R	L	K	E	S	T	R	E	L	B	A	R	N	O	W	L
B	J	A	C	K	D	A	W	F	I	T	L	S	A	K	W	O	P
L	A	M	R	A	R	S	R	I	O	N	U	P	V	A	T	E	R
A	Y	I	O	C	I	P	E	A	W	I	E	L	E	L	N	A	E
C	T	E	W	T	T	A	N	I	G	H	T	I	N	G	A	L	E
K	T	H	L	O	N	R	P	S	A	G	I	N	U	M	O	B	N
B	A	W	N	L	Q	R	K	F	N	Z	T	I	P	V	D	A	J
I	Z	I	S	K	O	O	S	L	N	I	N	F	J	Q	U	T	L
R	C	O	S	H	R	W	E	P	E	L	I	C	A	N	E	R	Y
D	U	C	K	T	A	N	H	P	T	H	R	U	S	H	A	O	R
O	R	T	Y	L	L	S	V	A	L	S	I	Y	R	E	G	S	E
T	L	Y	L	T	D	C	S	R	M	L	D	S	A	C	L	S	D
G	E	O	A	R	U	K	W	T	P	M	A	G	P	I	E	O	S
O	W	I	R	C	N	A	I	R	H	P	E	E	U	G	L	S	T
L	R	D	K	I	N	G	F	I	S	H	E	R	O	N	P	O	A
D	L	O	P	O	O	I	T	D	C	V	S	O	L	Z	U	R	R
F	O	L	O	O	C	T	A	G	A	S	V	B	N	C	F	P	T
I	T	V	S	K	K	F	U	E	K	J	T	I	A	D	F	A	L
N	L	E	E	D	B	I	P	I	G	E	O	N	U	R	I	M	T
C	H	A	F	F	I	N	C	H	Q	U	X	O	L	S	N	A	D
H	L	M	S	T	P	O	Y	R	S	T	A	R	L	I	N	G	K

Our Cabana

Miss a turn to try Mexican food - Enchiladas.

Visit a Mexican Market go on 2 squares

this way

Start

visiting

going home

THE ULTIMA JOU

by Ann Moynihan

Learn to say Hello in Spanish (Hola!) go on 2 squares

Buy a Mexican hat to take home go on 1 square

PAC

Leave your photographs at home - Miss a turn while you go back for them.

Forget your passport. go back 2 squares

Leave your photographs at home - Miss a turn while you go back for them.

ME

Learn to ski go on 1 square

Can you imagine it? A journey round the world to visit all four of our World Centres – the special Guiding houses which belong to every one of us! Well, you might have to wait a while for the real thing, but why not visit all four in our board game? Up to four people can play, and all you need is a die and a counter for each player. Each player chooses a different World Centre as a starting point, and puts her counter on the right 'start' triangle. Each player has to throw a six to start, but does not move until her next go, when she moves the number of squares shown on the die for that go. Once you are moving, the object of the game is to travel round

this way

Our Chalet

going home

visiting

Start

Swap your County badge for a Swiss Little Bee

Miss a turn to try a Swiss Fond